n' Tatties

DAE IT YERSEL'

THISTLE
STREET P.S

Better Beasties Vet Clinic

This book belongs to

_____

_____

Picture Kelpies is an imprint of Floris Books
First published in 2012 by Floris Books
Third printing 2014
Text © Mike Nicholson
Illustrations © Claire Keay

The publisher acknowledges subsidy from Creative Scotland towards
the publication of this volume. British Library CIP Data available
ISBN 978-086315-910-7
Printed in China through Asia Pacific Offset Ltd

Thistle Street

A braw Scots story for bairns

MIKE NICHOLSON
AND CLAIRE KEAY

Hello! It's so good to have you along.
Welcome to Thistle Street!
There are pretty wee houses with bright painted doors,
and lots of new people to meet.

Look closely you'll see there's all sorts going on,
so let's take some time as we wander.
You might even learn some new words on the way,
in places where we'll have a *daunder*.

People bustle about at the start of the day,
all rushing from A on to B.
Some are going to work, some are off to the shops,
there's plenty of life here to see.

Jamie's pelting to school on his shiny new scooter,
speeding along with a flash.
But he hasn't yet learned how to stop – so watch out!
Stand by for a massive...

... stramash!

Lewis the artist is out with his easel.
He's trying to capture the street.
Brushes fly, colours splash this way and that,
though his painting stays beautifully neat.

The school bell has gone but the Ross twins don't hear it,
they gaze at the picture in awe.
"That's bonnie," says Mairi, who loves to paint too,
and Hamish agrees, saying, *"braw!"*

Ramsay's the Baker is right on the corner;
there's always a great buzz of voices.
It's time for a fresh batch of bread, baps and buns:
look at the wonderful choices!

The baking's so fine, people stand here for ages,
queuing whatever the weather.
They're happy to wait for a pastry or cake,
as they all get to have a good *blether*.

Mr McKay, the village greengrocer,
isn't the happiest man.
The vegetable garden outside his back door
hasn't been growing to plan.

You might think it cuddly, and even quite sweet
to have visits each day from a rabbit.
But finding your carrots all nibbled and gnawed
is more likely to make you feel *crabbit*.

Mr Campbell sells hardware
of every kind,
he has hammers and light bulbs
and screws.
Hundreds of boxes,
all neatly on shelves,
hold everything you'd ever use.

His old till's the one thing that isn't quite right,
though for adding it's still a big help.
But sometimes the cash drawer gets stuck and won't open,
until it's been given a *skelp*.

At school Miss Dunbar and her class have been working,
inventing a new kind of treat:
With oatmeal and raisins and breadcrumbs and fat,
it's a cake that the birds love to eat.

But instead of a beak and a flutter of wings,
there's the flash of a tail, grey and bushy –
A squirrel thief, pinching some food on the run,
causes a bit of a *stushie!*

Big Euan is Thistle Street's strongman.
He can lift up a horse like a dog.

His plan for today is a huge caber toss –
a record for throwing that log.

With a skip and a twirl as part of his run,
Euan's making his sport look quite arty.

But his fancy new moves leave him all in a spin:
he trips over and gets himself *clarty*.

Down at the vet's, Jeannie's morning was spent
giving patients the best of her care.
She's fed them and brushed them and given them jags,
now they're out for some afternoon air.

But walking three dogs is tricky to do
when they scamper around by your ankle.
A cat passing by makes matters much worse,
now they've all ended up in a *fankle*.

Agnes Auld has been busy since early today,
giving Thistle Street's houses a clean.
Number 10's in a mess but she's still going strong,
leaving things with a sparkling sheen.

She wipes, dusts and polishes all that she sees,
even hoovering wee budgie Dougal.
To be thorough she hangs every carpet outside
and gives them a really good *shoogle*.

By mid-afternoon, the dark clouds roll in:
it looks like it's going to pour.
The Docherty children all race home from school,
but they're soaked when they reach
the front door.

The rain hammers down so they're all stuck inside.
This weather could just make them shriek.
But jigsaws and drawing and reading good books
keep them happy on days when it's *dreich*.

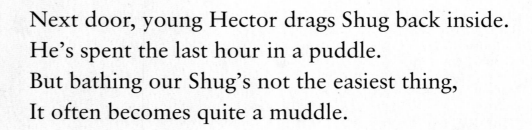

Next door, young Hector drags Shug back inside.
He's spent the last hour in a puddle.
But bathing our Shug's not the easiest thing,
It often becomes quite a muddle.

Soon bubbles are flying and waves hit the floor,
the mess is quite something to look at.
When Shug ends it all with a mighty big shake,
it's Hector who's totally *drookit*.

The rain's stopped, but now, as the sun starts to set,
Thistle Street's shadows stretch longer.
Soon darkness is deepening, stars prick the sky,
the moon rises high and glows stronger.

Say 'goodbye' to all of the people we've met,
as our visit here soon will have ceased.
In each house it's now time for curtains and sleep,
and for all mums and dads to say, '*wheesht!*'

Better Beasties Vet Clinic

Blether – a chat, to chat
Braw – fine, attractive,
    splendid
Clarty – messy, dirty

Crabbit – bad tempered, grumpy
Daunder – a stroll, to stroll
Dreich – dreary, dismal,
    miserable

Drookit – extremely wet, soaked
Fankle – a tangle, a muddle
Shoogle – a shake, to shake or rock
Skelp – a smack, to slap

Stramash – an uproar, a disturbance
Stushie – a state of excitement or
   anxiety
Wheesht – be quiet!